SPOTLIGHT on MUSIC

PRODUCTION

PIANO ACCOMPANIMENTS

TEXAS

Grade 1

Series Authors

Judy Bond	Betsy M. Henderson	Nancy L.T. Miller
René Boyer	John Jacobson	Ivy Rawlins
Margaret Campbelle-Holman	Michael Jothen	Susan Snyder
Emily Crocker	Chris Judah-Lauder	Gilberto D. Soto
Marilyn C. Davidson	Carol King	
Robert de Frece	Vincent P. Lawrence	**Kodály Contributing Consultant**
Virginia Ebinger	Ellen McCullough-Brabson	Sr. Lorna Zemke
Mary Goetze	Janet McMillion	

Macmillan McGraw-Hill

HAL•LEONARD®

NOTE TO THE TEACHER

You asked for it—you got it! Now, for the first time ever, the new piano arrangements for Spotlight on Music™ replicate the vocal and instrumental arrangement on the song recordings. This time-saving feature ensures a seamless transition from the recorded performance to the classroom experience with respect to the harmonic structure, from, and style of the song.

For support in teaching choreography, use the following segments from the Grade-Level DVD:
*   **John Jacobson**, which demonstrates selected songs' choreography in front, back, and split screen views.
*   **Music Theatre International**, in which Broadway for Kids choreography is presented in several formats, including a slower tempo and a teaching segment of specific choreography details.

The Grade-Level DVD booklet offers additional support with a glossary of choreographed movements and terms related to stage movements.

Choreography notes for the songs in the Broadway for Kids musical are provided by Music Theatre International. Choreography notes for all other songs are written by John Jacobson.

The McGraw·Hill Companies

Macmillan McGraw-Hill

Published by Macmillan/McGraw-Hill, of McGraw-Hill Education, a division of The McGraw-Hill Companies, Inc., Two Penn Plaza, New York, New York, 10121

Printed in the United States of America

ISBN: 0-02-295904-1

3 4 5 6 7 8 9 066 09 08 07 06 05

Texas in the Spotlight Contents

Salute to Texas Medley

The Yellow Rose of Texas
Traditional Folk Song
Deep in the Heart of Texas
Words by June Hershey
Music by Don Swandor

Tilting claps

There's a yel - low rose in Tex - as, I'm go - ing there to
(2.) sweet - est lit - tle rose - bud that Tex - as ev - er

v1: Wipe like "safe" in baseball   Tap head with R index finger   Wipe like "safe" in baseball
v2: Shimmy jazz hands by the side of your head

see, No oth - er fel - low knows her, no - bod - y else but
knew. Her eyes are bright as dia - monds, they spark - le like the

Deep in the Heart of Texas, Words by June Hershey.
Music by Don Swander. Copyright © 1941 by Melody
Lane Publications, Inc. Copyright Renewed. International
Copyright Secured. All Rights Reserved.

Texas, Our Texas

Words by Gladys Yoakum Wright and William J. Marsh
Music by William J. Marsh
Piano Accompaniment by MMH

1. Tex - as, our Tex - as! All hail the might - y State!
3. Tex - as, our Tex - as! From ty - rant grip now free,

Coda
(♩ = 115)
R hand to heart

God bless you Tex - as! And keep you brave and strong, That

you may grow in pow'r and worth, Through - out the ag — es long!

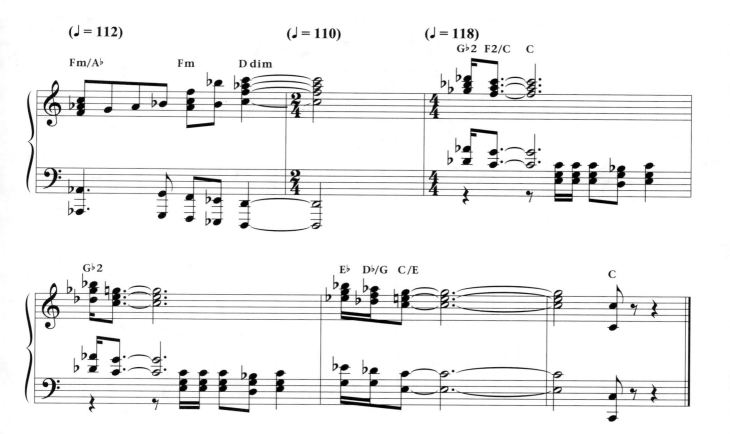

Teacher's Notes

A be ce
(A B C)

Latin American Folk Song
Adapted by Jenny Wells Vincent
Piano Accompaniment by Larry Moore

TEACHER'S PAGE T213

1

A la rueda rueda
('Round and 'Round)

Latin American Folk Song
English Version by MMH
Piano Accompaniment by Larry Moore

Spanish: A la rue - da rue - da,
English: 'Round and 'round and 'round, sweet

pan y ca - ne - la; to - ma tu chi - ni - ta, é - cha - la_a la_es -
cin - na - mon and sweet rolls. Take your lit tle child, and send her to the

cue - la; si no quie - re ir, é - cha - la_a dor - mir con la yer - ba
school - room. If she will not go, may - be she's a - sleep! With a leaf of

2

bue - na   y_el to - ron - jil.   Tu - rum - bé,   tu - rum - bé,   sen - ta - di - to
spear - mint,   sweet lem - on balm,   Tu - rum - bé,   Tu - rum - bé,   sit - ting down, and

me que - dé.
down I stay!

A Tisket, A Tasket

Traditional Children's Song from the Virgin Islands
Collected by Karen Ellis
Piano Accompaniment by Stacey Nordmeyer

A tis - ket, a tas - ket, a

green and yel - low bas - ket; I wrote a let - ter to my mom and on the way I dropped it.

T - I - M - E time to drop it, T - I - M - E time to drop it, T - I - M - E time to drop it.

Acka Backa

TEACHER'S PAGE T256

Playground Game
Piano Accompaniment by Larry Moore

Ack - a back - a so - da crack - er, Ack - a back - a boo!

Ack - a back - a so - da crack - er, Out goes you!

¡Adivina lo que es!
(Guess What It Is!)

Traditional Mexican Riddle
English Version MMH
Piano Accompaniment by Larry Moore

TEACHER'S PAGE T170

Spanish: Ti - to Ti - to ca - po - ti - to. Su - be al cie - lo y pe - ga un gri - to.
English: Ti - to, Ti - to Ca - po - ti - to, Fly up in the sky and shout there.

¡A - di - vi - na lo que es!
Can you guess what it might be?

1. Cohe - te cohe - te.
Sky - rock - et! Sky - rock - et!

2. Cohe - te cohe - te.
Sky - rock et! Sky - rock et!

All Night, All Day

TEACHER'S PAGE T232

African American Spiritual
Piano Accompaniment by Larry Moore

America

Words by Henry Carey
Music by Samuel F. Smith
Piano Accompaniment by Tom Anderson

Stand with R hand on heart

My coun-try 'tis of thee, Sweet land of lib - er-ty, Of thee I sing.

Move R hand from L to R with palm up *Scoop L hand to shoulder level*

Land where my fa - thers died, Land of the Pil - grim's pride,

Bring both hands over head *Clap hands together and bring to heart level**

From ev - 'ry___ moun - tain-side Let___ free - dom ring.

*After lyrics: bring hands up and "burst" hands open. On last beat, bring R hand back to heart.

8

The Animal Song

TEACHER'S PAGE T288

American Folk Song
Piano Accompaniment by Larry Moore

1. Al - li - ga - tor, hedge - hog, ant - eat - er, bear,
2. Bull - frog,____ wood - chuck, wol - ve - rine,____ goose,
3. Mud____ tur - tle, whale,____ glow - worm,____ bat,
4. Black____ squir - rel, ea - gle, pel - i - can,____ doe,

Rat - tle - snake, buf - fa - lo, an - a - con - da, hare.
Whip - por - will, chip - munk, jack - rab - bit, moose.
Sal - a snail,____ Mal - tese____ cat.
chick - a - dee, pea - cock,

bob - o - link and crow.

The Ants Go Marching

TEACHER'S PAGE T22

Music adapted from
When Johnny Comes Marching Home by Patrick S. Gilmore
Piano Accompaniment by Larry Moore

ants go march - ing one by one.
ants go march - ing two by two.
ants go march - ing three by three.
ants go march - ing four by four.
Hur - rah!_____ Hur -

rah!_____
The ants go march - ing one by one.
The ants go march - ing two by two.
The ants go march - ing three by three.
The ants go march - ing four by four.
Hur -

Lit - tle   one   stops   to   say   "THE   END!"

5. The ants go marching five by five. . .
   The little one stops to take a dive. . .

6. The ants go marching six by six. . .
   The little one stops to pick up sticks. . .

7. The ants go marching seven by seven. . .
   The little one stops to pray to Heaven. . .

8. The ants go marching eight by eight. . .
   The little one stops to make them late. . .

9. The ants go marching nine by nine. . .
   The little one stops to kill some time. . .

Apples and Bananas

TEACHER'S PAGE T151

Traditional
Piano Accompaniment by Anna Marie Spallina

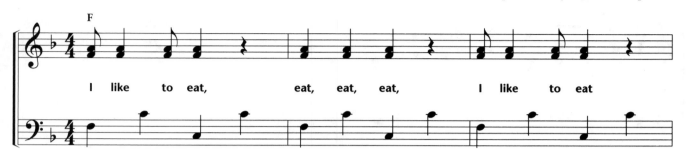

I like to eat, eat, eat, eat, I like to eat

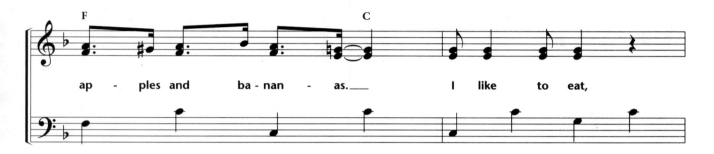

ap - ples and ba - nan - as.___ I like to eat,

eat, eat, eat, I like to eat, ap - ples and ba - nan - as.___

2. I like to āt, āt, āt.
   I like to āt āpples and bānānās...

3. I like to ēt...ēpples and bēnēnēs...

4. I like to īt...īpples and bīnīnīs...

5. I like to ōt...ōpples and bōnōnōs...

6. I like to ūt...ūpples and būnūnūs...

(Repeat Verse 1)

Arre, mi burrito
(Gid' yup, Little Burro)

Latin American Folk Song
English words by MMH
Piano Accompaniment by Larry Moore

TEACHER'S PAGE T257

Spanish: A - rre, mi bu -
English: Gid - 'yup, lit - tle

rri - to, que va - mos a Be - lén.
bur - ro, we're go - ing to Be - lén.

Que ma - ña - na es fies - ta y el o - tro tam - bién.
Fies - ta is to - mor - row, and next day a - gain.

Autumn Leaves

Anonymous
Piano Accompaniment by Kryste Andrews

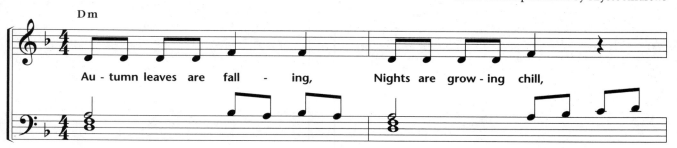

Au - tumn leaves are fall - ing, Nights are grow - ing chill,

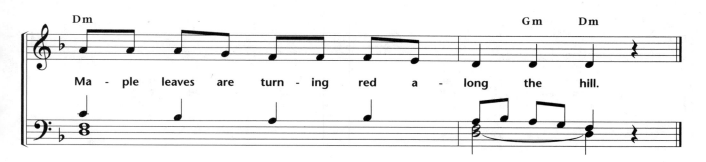

Ma - ple leaves are turn - ing red a - long the hill.

Autumn Leaves are Falling

TEACHER'S PAGE T330

Words and Music by Mary Donnelly
Piano Accompaniment by Larry Moore

1. Au - tumn leaves are fall - ing, fall - ing to the ground,
2. Au - tumn leaves are fall - ing, fall - ing through the air,
3. Au - tumn leaves are fall - ing, fall - ing from the sky,

paint - ing all the hill - side yel - low, red and brown.
leav - ing gold - en trea - sure ly - ing ev - 'ry - where.
whis - p'ring to the wild geese, "It is time to fly."

Beau - ti - ful are the au - tumn leaves.

Beau - ti - ful are the au - tumn leaves.

The Bear Went Over the Mountain

Traditional
Piano Accompaniment by Anna Marie Spallina

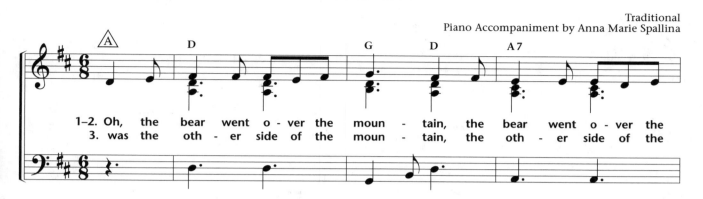

1–2. Oh, the bear went o - ver the moun - tain, the bear went o - ver the
3. was the oth - er side of the moun - tain, the oth - er side of the

moun - tain, the bear went o - ver the moun - tain, to see what he could see.____
moun - tain, the oth - er side of the moun - tain, was all that he could see.____

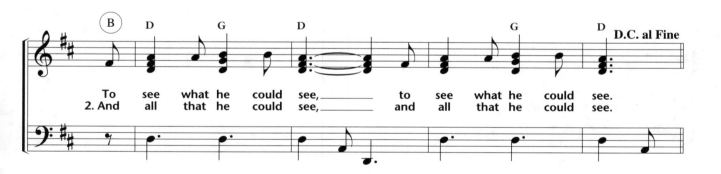

To see what he could see,____ to see what he could see.
2. And all that he could see,____ and all that he could see.

17

Bee, Bee, Bumblebee

American Rhyme
Music by Marilyn Copeland Davidson
Piano Accompaniment by Larry Moore

Bee, bee, bum - ble - bee, Stung a man up - on his knee,

Stung a pig up - on his snout, I de - clare that you are out.

18

Best Friends

TEACHER'S PAGE T222

Words and Music by
Sandor Slomovitz
Piano Accompaniment by Larry Moore

Refrain

Hold a friend's hand and walk in place

Best friends, al-ways to-geth-er, best friends,

ne-ver a-lone.___ Best friends, e-ven when we're a-part,___

best friends, deep in the heart.___ Oh,___ we're best friends,

deep in the heart. You help me see my way through thick and thin, — no

mat - ter where I go. When I think of you, I am

nev - er lost, and that's how I know,

that's how you show that we're

Big and Small

Used as listening only
TEACHER'S PAGE T200

Words and Music by Ellen McCullough Brabson
Piano Accompaniment by Larry Moore

El - e - phants are big. Spi - ders are small.

How can a spi - der's web hold them all?

*Song is included here for listening reference only.
Children do not sing in the lesson.

Bluebells

American Jump-Rope Song
Piano Accompaniment by Larry Moore

Blue - bells, cock - le shells,
ee - vy, i - vy o - ver - head. My moth - er said that I was born in Jan - u - ar - y, Feb - ru - ar - y,
March, A - pril, May, June, Ju - ly, Au - gust, Sep - tem - ber, Oct - o - ber, No -

vem - ber,   De - cem - ber.

Bonjour, mes amis
(Hello, My Friends)

TEACHER'S PAGE T18

Cajun Folk Song
Piano Accompaniment by Larry Moore

French: Bon - jour, mes a - mis, bon -
English: Hel - lo, my friends, hel -

jour. Bon - jour, mes a - mis, bon - jour. Bon - jour, mes a - mis, bon -
lo. Hel - lo, my friends, hel - lo. Hel - lo, my friends, hel -

jour, mes a - mis, Bon - jour, mes a - mis, bon - jour. Bon - jour, mes a - mis.
lo, my friends, Hel - lo, my friends, hel - lo. Hel - lo, my good friends.

24

Boris, the Singing Bear

Words and Music by Jackie Silberg
Piano Accompaniment by Larry Moore

(Sing sadly and slowly)
(Sing joyfully)

1. There was a bear named Bo - ris who sang in the an - i - mal cho - rus. He sang so loud he drew a crowd and the peo - ple cheered for Bo - ris.
2. One day that bear named Bo - ris was not in the an - i - mal cho - rus. He wasn't a - round and couldn't be found And the peo - ple cried for Bo - ris.
3. At win - ter's end the fo - rest came alive with the an - i - mal cho - rus. The peo - ple cheered "Oh, look who's here! That sing - ing bear named Bo - ris!"
4. Where have you been dear Bo - ris? Why wer - en't you in the cho - rus? "I had a date to hi - ber - nate in a cave out in the fo - rest."

Refrain

Sing Bo - ris sing. Sing your bear song for us.

Sing your song and we'll hum a - long as we all march through the for - est.

One for - est.

26

Brinca la tablita
(Hop, Hop!)

TEACHER'S PAGE T71

Puerto Rican Folk Song
English Version by MMH
Piano Accompaniment by Larry Moore

Spanish: Brin - ca la ta - bli - ta, ya yo la brin - qué.
English: Hop on the ta - bli - ta, I have had my turn.

Brín - ca - la tu a - ho - ra que yo me can - sé.
Hop a - cross, it's your turn now, and I am tired.

Brush Your Teeth

TEACHER'S PAGE T66

Adapted and Arranged by Louise Dain and Raffi
Piano Accompaniment by Larry Moore

1. When you   wake up   in   the   morn-ing and it's   quar-ter to   one___   And you
(2.)   wake up   in   the   morn-ing and it's   quar-ter to   two___   And you
(3.)   wake up   in   the   morn-ing and it's   quar-ter to   three___   And your
(4.)   wake up   in   the   morn-ing and it's   quar-ter to   four___   And you

want   to   have   a   lit - tle   fun
want   to   find____   some-thing to   do,
mind   starts   hum-ming   twid - dle de   dee,   you brush your teeth, ch, ch, ch, ch,   ch,
think   you   hear   a   knock on your   door,

*You may wish to have children speak this phrase.

Butterfly, Flutter By

TEACHER'S PAGE T333

Words and Music by Linda Worsley
Piano Accompaniment by Larry Moore

With pedal

But-ter-fly, flut-ter by, Flut-ter and fly, Col-or-ful wings will car-ry you high!

But-ter-fly, flut-ter by, Flut-ter a - way, Wish that you could stay! But-ter-

fly, flut - ter by, but-ter - fly. But - ter - fly.

Wish that you could stay!

30

Caribbean Amphibian

Words and Music by Mark Saltzman
Piano Accompaniment by Mark Brymer

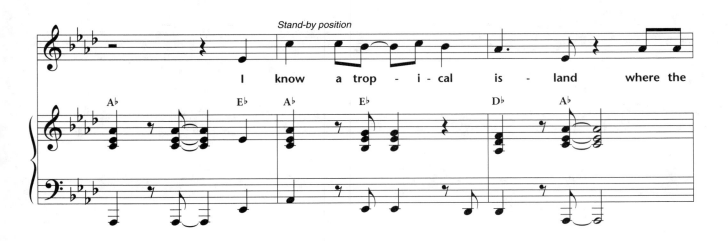

Stand-by position

I know a trop - i - cal is - land where the

man - go moon___ and ba - na - na sun shine and on this trop - i - cal

is - land there lives a cous - in of mine. Some -

Shrug   *Stand-by position*

times he lives___ in the wa - ter. Some - times he lives___ on the

v 1: Hold arms out to sides, palms out, like a sunbather
v 2: Pretend to play guitar

land. { Some - times he likes___ to go sun him - self on
{ Some - times he likes___ to play mu - sic in an

soft Car - ib - be-an sand.
all am-phib - i - an band. He's a Car - ib - be-an___ am - phib - i - an. He

likes to hop in the trop-i-cal sea. Car - ib - be-an___ am-phib-i-an, a

frog in a co-co-nut tree. Some

Traveling arms to the L, then to the R

Limp wrists at chest level, like frog legs
2nd time to Coda
Slap legs Clap Present high Slowly lower hands to sides

D.S. al Coda

33

Categories

Traditional Childrens Game
Piano Accompaniment by Larry Moore

Chang
(Elephant)

TEACHER'S PAGE T198

Thai Folk Song
Collected and Transcribed by Kathy B. Sorensen
Piano Accompaniment by Anna Marie Spallina

Thai: chang chang chang chang chang nɔng kəi hɛn chang ru
English: Chang, chang, chang, chang, chang, Oh have you seen or

plau chang man tʋa to maḷ bau ja mug yau yau rḷəg wa ngʋang mik kiu taḷ
not? Two tusks, a long, long nose be-tween, a "trunk" they call it! He has two

ngʋang rḷəg wa nga mi hu mi ta hang yau
ears and two eyes,___ And such a long, long___ tail.

Charlie Over the Ocean

TEACHER'S PAGE T75

Singing Game
Piano Accompaniment by Larry Moore

Char - lie o - ver the o - cean,   (Char - lie o - ver the o - cean,)
Char - lie caught_ a black - bird,   (Char - lie caught_ a black - bird,)

Char - lie o - ver the sea._____   (Char - lie o - ver the sea,)_____
Can't____ catch____ me,   (Can't____ catch____ me.)_____

Leader   *Group*

Leader   *Group*   **4th time To Coda**

2nd time D.S. al Coda

Coda

38

Chase the Squirrel

TEACHER'S PAGE T88

American Game Song
Piano Accompaniment by Larry Moore

1. Round up four and chase the squirrel, chase the squirrel, chase the squirrel.
2. Break and swing and chase the squirrel, chase the squirrel, chase the squirrel.
3. Round up six and chase the squirrel, chase the squirrel, chase the squirrel.
4. Break and swing and chase the squirrel, chase the squirrel, chase the squirrel.

Round up four and chase the squirrel, way down be - low.
Break and swing and chase the squirrel, way down be - low.
Round up six and chase the squirrel, way down be - low.
Break and swing and chase the squirrel, way down be

low.

39

Chickery Chick

Music by Sidney Lippman
Words by Sylvia Dee
Piano Accompaniment by Larry Moore

Once there lived a chick-en who would say "chick-chick," _____ "Chick-chick" _____ all day. Soon that chick got sick and tired of just "chick-chick," _____ So one morn-ing he start-ed to say: "Chick-er-y chick, cha-la, cha-la, Check-a-la rome-y in a ba-nan-i-ka, Bol-li-ka, wol-li-ka, can't you see Chick-er-y chick is me."

40

Clap Your Hands

American Folk Song
Piano Accompaniment by Larry Moore

1. Clap, clap, clap your hands,
2. Stamp, stamp, stamp your feet,
3. Nod, nod, nod your heads,

Clap your hands to - geth - er,   Clap, clap, clap your hands,
Stamp them all to - geth - er,   Stamp, stamp, stamp your feet,
Nod them all to - geth - er,   Nod, nod, nod your heads,

Clap your hands to - geth - er.
Stamp them all to - geth - er.
Nod them all to - geth - er.

Come Back, My Little Chicks

TEACHER'S PAGE T134

Hungarian Children's Game
Adapted by Jill Trinka and Rhona Brink
Piano Accompaniment by Larry Moore

Come back home, my lit - tle chicks.

We won't come. Why not? Of the wolf. Where's he hid - ing?
We're a - fraid. Of what? In the woods. What's he do - ing?

Wash - ing. Where's he wash-ing? By the stream. What's he dry his face on?

On the kit - ty cat's tail!

Cookies

TEACHER'S PAGE T277

Words by Robert Reale
Music by Willie Reale

Cook-ies, cook-ies, cook-ies, cook-ies, We go koo-y eat-ing cook-ies, We will nev-er stop—

R index finger counts fingers on L hand

Let's have more, more,

L index counts on R

Drop hands

Fists punch straight up

more cook - ies!

Counting Song

TEACHER'S PAGE T195

Mexican Folk Song
Piano Accompaniment by Anna Marie Spallina

Spanish/English: U - no, dos y tres, cua - tro, cin - co, seis;

sie - te, o - cho, nue - ve, I can count to diez.

Refrain

La la la la la, la la la l ala, la la la la la la;

la la la la la, la la la la la, la la la la la la.

47

Cut the Cake

TEACHER'S PAGE T232

American Game Song
Piano Accompaniment by Stacey Nordmeyer

Clap your hands to - geth - er,   Give your - self a   shake.

Make a hap - py cir - cle,   Then you cut the   cake.

Dance Myself to Sleep

Music by Christopher Cerf
Words by Norman Stiles
Piano Accompaniment by Mark Brymer

tap - pin' to taps and I'm a - rar - in' to snooze.

Stand tall

C   C dim 7   C   C/G

D.S. al Coda

3. Well   I'm

E♭ dim 7/G   C   C   B♭/C   C7

Coda   *Thumbs to self*   *Hands under head like pillow*

we'll   dance   our - selves   to   sleep,   oh   yeah!___

G7   C13   F6   D7

Diana
(Play the Bugle)

TEACHER'S PAGE T334

Mexican Folk Song
Piano Accompaniment by Larry Moore

Spanish: Dia - na, dia - na pa - ra tí a Jua - na.
English: Play the bu - gle play for ti - a Juan - a.

Dia - na, dia - na pa - ra tío Joa - quín.
Play the bu - gle play for tío Joa - quín.

Un - re - bo - zo lle - va e - lla,
On her head she wears a shawl, and

un som - bre - ro lle - va él.
On his head he wears a hat.

Dia - na, dia - na pa - ra tí a Jua - na.
Play the bu - gle play for tí a Jua - na.

dia - na, dia - na pa - ra tío Joa - quín. ¡Hey!
Play the bu - gle play for tío Joa - quín. Hey!

Diou Shou Juan'er
(Hide the Handkerchief)

TEACHER'S PAGE T212

Chinese Game Song
Transcribed by Kathy B. Sorensen
English Words by Linda Worsley
Piano Accompaniment by Larry Moore

Chinese Pronunciation: di o sho juər di o sho juər

English: **Hide the hand-ker-chief! Hide the hand-ker-chief!**

chıng chıng di fang tsai shau pʌng yo di

Ev-er so soft-ly, Put it down be-

ho miər da jya bu uao gao su

hind a friend. No-one tell {him where it {her

ta kwai diər kwa diər jwa ju ta

is. Quick-ly, quick-ly, catch {him now! {her

Down by the Bay

TEACHER'S PAGE T48

American Folk Song
Piano Accompaniment by Larry Moore

say,

1. "Did you
2. "Did you
3. "Did you
4. "Did you
5. "Did you
6. "Did you

ev - er see a goose _____ kiss - ing a moose
ev - er see a whale with a pol - ka dot _____ tail,
ev - er see a fly _____ wear - ing a tie,
ev - er see a bear _____ comb - ing his hair,
ev - er see _____ lla - mas eat - ing their pa - ja - mas,
ev - er have a time when you could - n't make a rhyme,

down by the bay?" Down by the bay."

Down the Hill

TEACHER'S PAGE T281

Words by Robert Reale
Music by Willie Reale

down the hill.

Down the hill go-ing fast-er. Head-ing straight for dis-as-ter. Watch the trees. Watch the boul-ders.

Tuck your knees   to your shoul-ders. Aaaaaah!

Duérmete mi niño
(Go to Sleep, My baby)

TEACHER'S PAGE T61

Puerto Rican Folk Song
Spanish Words and Arrangement by José-Lúis Orozco
English Version by MMH
Piano Accompaniment by Larry Moore

Spanish: Duér - me - te mi ni - ño,
English: Sleep my lit - tle ba - by;

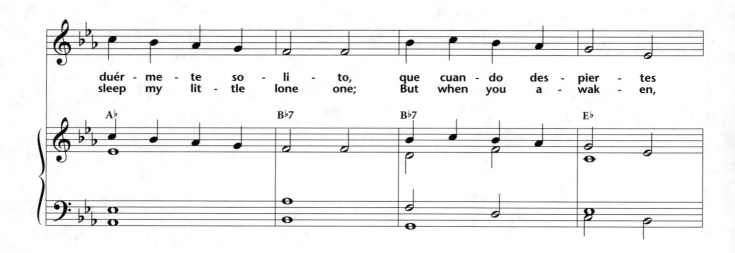

duér - me - te so - li - to, que cuan - do des - pier - tes
sleep my lit - tle lone one; But when you a - wak - en,

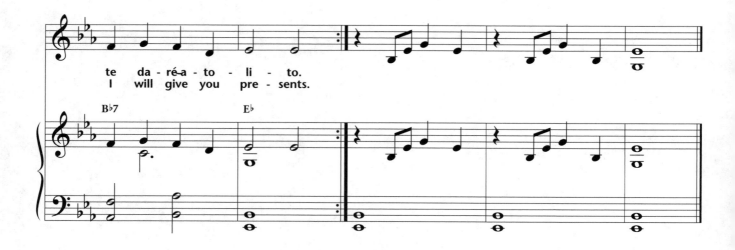

te da - ré a - to - li - to.
I will give you pre - sents.

El florón
(The Flower)

TEACHER'S PAGE T117

Traditional Puerto Rican Game Song
Arranged by Alejandro Jimenez
Piano Accompaniment by Larry Moore

Spanish: El flo - rón, pa - só por a - quí, y yo no lo
English: El flo - rón, pass it all a - round, Now it can't be

vi, y yo no lo vi. El flo - vi. Que
found, Now it can't be found! El flo - found. Where

pa - se, que pa - se, que pa se el flo - rón. Que rón.
is it? where is it? I can't see it now! It now!

El juego chirimbolo
(The Chirimbolo Game)

TEACHER'S PAGE T103

Ecuadorian Game Song
Adapted and Arranged by Elizabeth Villarreal Brennan
Piano Accompaniment by Larry Moore

Spanish: El jue - go chi - rim - bo - lo,
English: The game of Chi - rim - bo - lo,

qué bo - ni - to es, con un pie, o - tro pie, u - na
What a lot of fun! With one foot, oth - er foot, with a

ma - no, o - tra ma - no; un co - do, o - tro co - do. El
hand,____ oth - er hand,____ an el - bow, oth - er el - bow. the

co - do; el jue - go chi - rim - bo - lo, qué bo - ni - to es.
el - bow. The game of Chi - rim - bo - lo, What a lot of fun!

64

El rorro
(The Babe)

TEACHER'S PAGE T356

Mexican Carol
English version by MMH
Piano Accompaniment by Larry Moore

Spanish: A la ru - ru - ru, ni - ño chi -
English: A la ru - ru - ru, My love - ly

qui - to, Duér - ma se ya,____ mi Je - su - si - to._____ Del e - le -
Je - sus, In sweet - est slum - ber now rest, my dear - est._____ You el - e -

fan - te has - ta el mos - qui - to, guar - den si - len - cio, no le ha - gan ru -
phant so huge, you small mos - qui - to, Be ver - y still, you must not wake our

i - do. A la ru -
Ni - ño. A la ru -

si - to.
dear - est.

Everybody Oughta Know

TEACHER'S PAGE T361

African American Song
Arranged by Ysaye Maria Barnwell
Piano Accompaniment by Larry Moore

George Washington

Words and Music by Lynn Freeman Olson
Piano Accompaniment by Stacey Nordmeyer

George Wash-ing-ton! George Wash-ing-ton!

He was a great, great man. When A-mer-i-cans won-dered who could

lead them, they said, "George Wash-ing-ton can!"

Gilly, Gilly, Gilly Good Morning

TEACHER'S PAGE T12

Traditional American Song
Piano Accompaniment by Larry Moore

During introduction, yawn, scratch ribs, stretch, pretend to wake up

Go a Tin
(Lantern Song)

TEACHER'S PAGE T363

Taiwanese Folk Song
English Version by MMH
Piano Accompaniment by Larry Moore

Pronunciation: go a tin go a tin
English: **Lan - tern bright, lan - tern tin bright,**

dai ge lai gya go a tin
Light the way, my lan - tern bright.

rit. 2nd time only

Goin' to the Zoo

TEACHER'S PAGE T192

Words and Music by Tom Paxton
Piano Accompaniment by Larry Moore

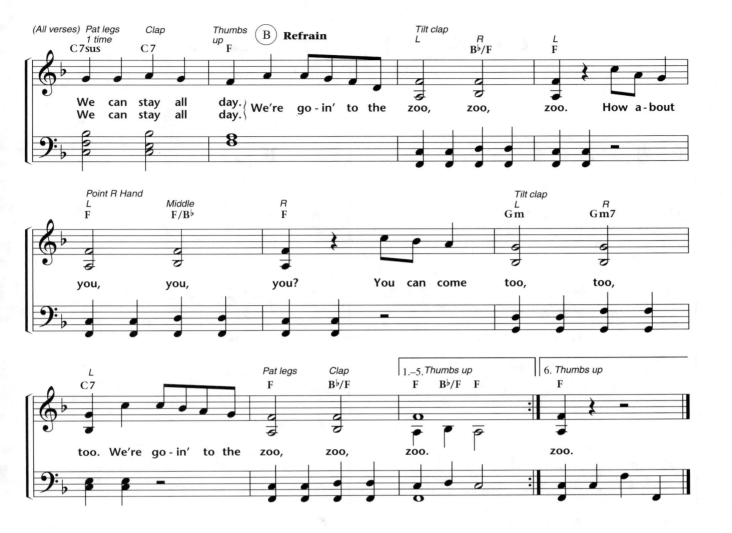

(During **Verse 3**: Act like a monkey)

3. See all the monkeys scritch,
     scritch, scratchin',
   Jumpin' all around and scritch,
     scritch, scratchin',
   Hangin' by their long tails,
     scritch, scritch, scratchin',
   We can stay all day. *Refrain*

(During **Verse 4**: Put paws up and
walk like a bear on its hind legs)

4. Big black bear all huff-a-puffin'
   Coat's too heavy, he's huff huff
     a -puffin',
   Don't get too near the
     huff huff-a-puffin',
   You can't stay all day. *Refrain*

(During **Verse 5**: Cross arms at
elbows and clap like seals' flippers)

5. Seals in the pool all honk,
     honk, honkin',
   Catchin' fish, and honk,
     honk, honkin'
   Little seals all honk,
     honk, honkin'
   We can stay all day. *Refrain*

(During **Verse 6**: Stretch and yawn)

6. We stayed all day, and I'm
     gettin' sleepy
   Gettin' sleepy, gettin' sleepy,
   Home already and I'm sleep,
     sleep, sleepy
   We have stayed all day. *Refrain*

Grasshoppers Three

TEACHER'S PAGE T284

American Folk Song
Piano Accompaniment by Larry Moore

The Green Grass Grew All Around

TEACHER'S PAGE T148

Traditional Children's Song
Piano Accompaniment by Larry Moore

* cumulative verses

2. And on that tree, …There was a limb, …
   The prettiest little limb, …That you ever did see, …
   The limb on the tree,
   And the tree in a hole, and the hole in the ground
   Sing Refrain

3. And on that limb, …There was a branch, …
   The prettiest little branch, …That you ever did see, …
   The branch on the limb, and the limb on the tree,
   And the tree in a hole, and the hole in the ground
   Sing Refrain

4. And on that branch, …There was a nest, …

5. And in that nest, …There was a egg, …

6. And in that egg, …There was a bird, …

7. And on the bird, …There was a wing, …

8. And on that wing, …There was a feather, …

9. And on the feather, …There was a bug, …

10. And on that bug, …There was a germ, …

Hakyo jong
(School Bells)

TEACHER'S PAGE T302

Words and Music by Mary Kimm Joh
English Version by MMH
Piano Accompaniment by Larry Moore

Pronunciation: ha kyo jong i dɛng dɛng dɛng ɔ sɔ mo i

English: Hear the school bells, ding, ding, ding! Chil - dren, hear the

ja sɔn sɛng ni mi u ɾi ɾʊl ki da ɾi shin da

call. Tea - cher will be at the door wait - ing for us all.

Halloween

Words and Music by Lynn Freeman Olson
Piano Accompaniment by Marilyn Christensen

You should know it's the time of year When the gob-lins and ghosts ap-pear. They come at night when there's no more light; Hal-low-een is al-most here. If you look ver-y care-ful-

ly,   There's a gob-lin be-hind that tree.   But   I   must   say,   don't   you

Dm   Gm

run   a - way,   'Cause   it   might   be   me!

Dm   Dm   A7   Dm

Hanukkah Chag Yafe
(Hanukkah Joyous Holiday)

TEACHER'S PAGE T350

Words and Music by Lewin Kipnis
Piano Accompaniment by Larry Moore

Hebrew
Pronunciation: xa nu ka   xa nu ka   xag yā fe kol kax
English: Ha - nuk - kah,   Ha - nuk - kah   Fes - ti - val of lights,

or xa viv   mi sa viv   gil lɛ ye led rach
Can - dle - light,   warm and bright,   sev - en days and nights.

xa nu ka   xa nu ka   sɛ vi von sov sov
Can - dles burn,   Drei - dels turn.   Ha - nuk - kah is here.

sov sov sov   sov sov sov   ma na im va tov
Spin, spin, spin,   spin, spin, spin,   Hap - py time of year!

The Happiest Street in the World

TEACHER'S PAGE T304

Words and Music by Joe Raposo
Piano Accompaniment by Mark Brymer

Clap on rest, then point
R hand at audience

Wag R index
finger at audience

1. If you feel lone - ly and you need a friend,
2. Some - times you wor - ry, you doubt and you fear,

Clap on rest, then put
both thumbs to chest

Point R index
finger at audience

I know a place on which you can de - pend.
but when you're with us those thoughts dis - ap - pear.

Stop with hands down

1 clap burst on "free"

place to be young, ___ a place to be free, for

A7   D13

Point both hands at audience, then thumbs to chest

Vaudeville Rocks

you and for me. ___ Yes, it's the hap-pi-est street ___ in the

Dm7   G7   C6

world. The hap-pi-est street ___ in a won-der-ful world. ___ Where-

Cmaj7   C6   B♭9

Head and Shoulders, Baby

TEACHER'S PAGE T40

African-American Street Game
As Sung by René Boyer-Alexander
Piano Accompaniment by Ian Williams

1. Head and shoul-ders, ba - by,

one, two, three. Head and shoul-ders, ba - by, one, two, three. Head and shoul-ders, head and
one, two, three. Knee and an - kle, ba - by, one, two, three. Knee and an - kle, knee and
one, two, three. Milk the cow, ba - by, one, two, three. Milk the cow, milk the
one, two, three. Throw the ball, ba - by, one, two, three. Throw the ball, throw the

shoul-ders, head and shoul-ders, ba - by, one, two, three. 2. Knee and an - kle, ba - by,
an - kle, knee and an - kle, ba - by, one, two, three. 3. Milk the cow, ba - by,
cow, milk the cow, ba - by, one, two, three. 4. Throw the ball, ba - by,
ball, throw the ball, ba - by, one, two, three.

86

Hello, There!

TEACHER'S PAGE T230

Call and Response Song

Hel - lo, there! (Hel -

lo, there!) How are you? (How are you?) It's so good (It's so good) To

see you. (To see you.) We'll sing and (We'll sing and) be

87

hap - py   (be hap - py) That we're all   here to - geth - er a -

gain.

Here We Come A-Wassailing

TEACHER'S PAGE T355

Engligh Carol
Piano Accompaniment by Marilyn Christensen

Verse

1. Here we come a - was - sail - ing a - mong the leaves so green,___
(2) are not dai - ly beg - gars that beg from door to door. We
(3) bless the mas - ter of this house, like - wise his mis - tress too, And

Here we come a - wan - d'ring so fair___ to be seen;
are your neigh - bor's chil - dren whom you have seen be - fore.
all the lit - tle chil - dren that round the ta - ble go.

Refrain

Love and joy come to you, And to you your was - sail too, And God

bless   you and   send___ you a hap   -   py New Year,   And God

send   you a hap - py New Year.

2. We
3. God   Year.

Here We Sit

TEACHER'S PAGE T251

American Singing Game
Piano Accompaniment by Stacey Nordmeyer

Here we sit in a ring. Close your eyes now while we sing.

One of us will go and hide. Guess who made that space so wide.

Hoo, Hoo!

TEACHER'S PAGE T55

Words and Music by Ethel Crowninshield
Piano Accompaniment by Larry Moore

Hop! Chirp! Moo!
Oh, Happy Springtime Day!

TEACHER'S PAGE T372

Words and Music by John Jacobson
and Alan Billingsley

(Spoken ad lib)
And that big old lazy cow just chews
her cud and lets out a big old mooooo.

Quack, quack, quack, moo,___ moo, moo, Hop, hop, chirp, quack,___

___ quack, moo, Oh, hap - py spring - time day.___

How Does Your Garden Grow?

TEACHER'S PAGE T144

Words and Music by
John Jacobson and John Higgins
Piano Accompaniment by Larry Moore

Hunt the Cows

TEACHER'S PAGE T236

Scandinavian Singing Game
Words by Jean Ritchie
Piano Accompaniment by Larry Moore

Wake up you sleep-y head and go and hunt the cat - tle,

Wake up you sleep-y head and go and hunt the cows.

The sun is hot,
I think I'll rest,

The cows are lost,
'Til they are come home.

99

I Am Slowly Going Crazy

TEACHER'S PAGE T127

Camp Song
Piano Accompaniment by Larry Moore

Lyrics:

I am slow-ly go-ing cra-zy, one two three four five six switch.

Cra-zy go-ing slow-ly am I, six five four three two one switch.

six five four three two one switch.

I Like Spinach

TEACHER'S PAGE T163

Traditional Children's Game
Piano Accompaniment by Larry Moore

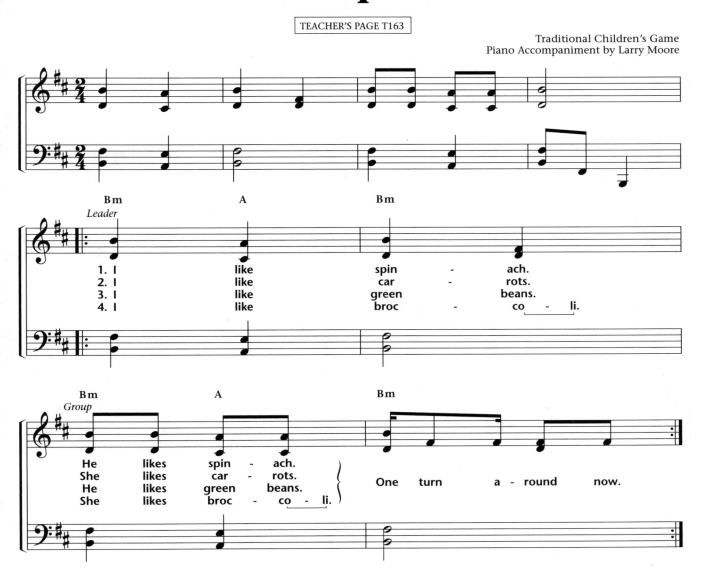

101

I Love My Country

TEACHER'S PAGE T328

Words and Music by Teresa Jennings
Piano Accompaniment by Larry Moore

I love my coun - try. I love my free - dom.

I love my flag and In - de - pen - dence Day.

I am a cit - i - zen. I have e - qual - i - ty.

I Wanna Be A Friend of Yours

TEACHER'S PAGE T84

American Singing Game
Piano Accompaniment by Larry Moore

104

If All the World Were Paper

TEACHER'S PAGE T296

English Folk Song
Piano Accompaniment by Larry Moore

all the world were pa - per and all the sea were

ink, if all the trees were bread and cheese, what

would we ev - er drink?

If

In My Little Motor Boat

TEACHER'S PAGE T159

Words and Music by Beatrice Krone and Ruth Heller
Piano Accompaniment by Larry Moore

It's So Nice On The Ice

TEACHER'S PAGE T346

Music and Words by Richard M. Sherman
and Robert B. Sherman
Piano Accompaniment by Larry Moore

It's so nice_____ on the ice,_____ As you

glide, glide, glide._____ It's so

nice_____ on the ice,_____ As you

slide,   slide,   slide. _____ Come a -

long, _____ come a - long, _____ Won't you

try   once   or   twice _____ And

see   how   it   feels   to   have   wings   on   your   heels?   It's   so

nice _____ on   the   ice. _____

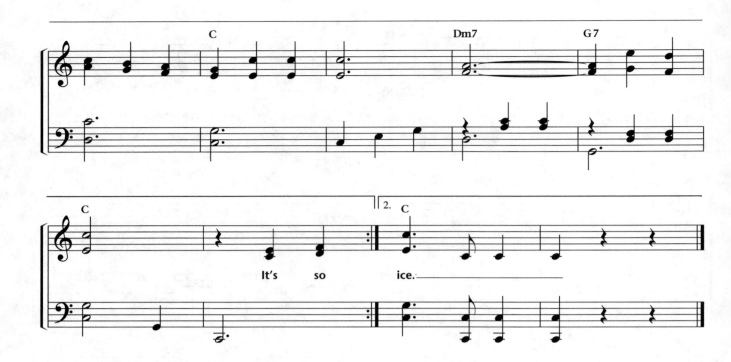

It's so ice.

I've a Pair of Fishes

TEACHER'S PAGE T124

Yiddish Folk Song
Words by Lillian Vandevere
Piano Accompaniment by Larry Moore

1. I've a pair of fish - es, fish - es. They are wash - ing
2. I've a pair of pup - pies, pup - pies. They are rais - ing
3. I've a pair of fox - es, fox - es. They are build - ing
4. I've a pair of bun - nies, bun - nies. They are read - ing
5. I've a pair of par - rots, par - rots. They are eat - ing

dish - es, dish - es.
gup - pies, gup - pies.
box - es, box - es.   This is in - deed a won - der.
fun - nies, fun - nies.
car - rots, car - rots.

Cumulative verse (no repeat first time)

See the fish - es   wash - ing   dish - es.
See the pup - pies   rais - ing   gup - pies.
See the fox - es   build - ing   box - es.   This is quite a
See the bun - nies   read - ing   fun - nies.
See the par - rots   eat - ing   car - rots.

D   A7   D   A7   D   A7

won - der,   this is quite a   won - der.

Bm7   A   D   A7   D

| 1.–4. |

won - der.

D   A7   D   A7   D

| 5. |

Jambo
(Hello)

TEACHER'S PAGE T230

Words and Music by Ella Jenkins
Piano Accompaniment by Larry Moore

Swahili: Jam - bo,___ jam - bo.___ Jam - bo sa - na, jam - bo.___
English: Hel - lo,___ hel - lo.___ Hel-lo ev-'ry - bod - y, hel - lo.___

Jam - bo sa - na, jam - bo.___
Hel-lo ev-'ry - bod - y, hel - lo.___

Jingle Bells

TEACHER'S PAGE T354

Words and Music by James Pierpont
Piano Accompaniment by Larry Moore

114

John the Rabbit

American Folk Game Song
Piano Accompaniment by Larry Moore

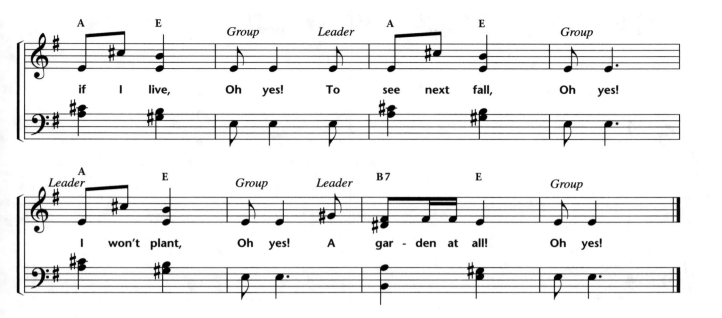

Johnny Works with One Hammer

TEACHER'S PAGE T96

American Singing Game
Piano Accompaniment by Tom Anderson

1. John-ny works with one ham-mer, one ham-mer,
2. John-ny works with two ham-mers, two ham-mers,
3. John-ny works with three ham-mers, three ham-mers,

one ham-mer, John-ny works with one ham-mer, Then he works with two.
two ham-mers, John-ny works with two ham-mers, Then he works with three.
three ham-mers, John-ny works with three ham-mers, Then he works with four.

4. Johnny works with four hammers,…Then he works with five.
5. Johnny works with five hammers,…Then he works no more.

118

Johnny's Flea

Traditional Folk Song
Piano Accompaniment by Larry Moore

One, two, three,   John-ny caught a flea.   Flea died, John-ny cried,   tee, hee, hee.

Jolly Old Saint Nicholas

TEACHER'S PAGE T352

American Carol
Piano Accompaniment by Larry Moore

v1: Hold stomach
v2: Use arms like a clock, bringing them together overhead by "twelve"
v3: Shrug L

v1: Lean R and cup R hand to ear
v2: Use hands like a pillow
v3: Shrug R

1. Jol - ly old Saint Nich - o - las, Lean your ear this way!
2. When the clock is strik - ing twelve, When I'm fast a - sleep,
3. John - ny wants a pair of skates; Su - zy wants a sled;

v1: Wag index finger
v2: Keep sleeping
v3: Pretend to hold a book

v1: R index finger to lips

Don't you tell a sin - gle soul What I'm go - ing to say;
Down the chim - ney broad and black, with your pack you'll creep.
Nel - lie wants a sto - ry - book, Yel - low, blue, and red.

120

Jump, Jim Joe

American Folk Song
Collected from Shirley Bates
Piano Accompaniment by Larry Moore

Kaeru no Uta
(Frog's Song)

Japanese Folk Song
English Version by MMH
Piano Accompaniment by Bill and Pat Medley

Pronunciation: ka e ru no u ta ga ki ko e te
English: **Hear the frog, he sings a song.** **It is such a**

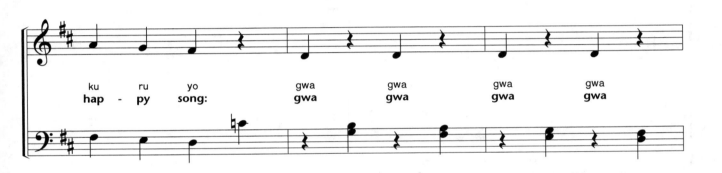

ku ru yo gwa gwa gwa gwa
hap - py song: **gwa** **gwa** **gwa** **gwa**

ge ro ge ro ge ro ge ro gwa gwa gwa
ge ro ge ro ge ro ge ro gwa gwa gwa.

123

Kari
(Wild Geese)

TEACHER'S PAGE T261

Japanese Folk Song
English Words by Florence White and Kazuo Akiyama
Piano Accompaniment by Larry Moore

Japanese Pronunciation: ka ri ka ri wa ta re
English: **Wild geese, wild geese, fly a - way!**

o ki na ka ri wa sa ki ni chi sa na ka ri wa
Big goose a - head of you leads the way, Small geese be - hind as you

a to ni na ka yo ku wa ta re
fly a - way. Peace - ful - ly, peace - ful - ly fly a - way.

Kobuta
(Piglet)

Japanese Children's Song
Collected by Margaret Campbelle-duGard
Piano Accompaniment by Bill and Pat Medley

TEACHER'S PAGE T167

Japanese Pronunciation:

1. ko bu ta   ta nu ki   ki tsu
2. bu bu bu   pon poko pon   kon kon

ne   ne ko   ko bu ta   ta nu
kon   nya o   bu bu bu   pon poko

ki   ki tsu ne   ne ko
pon   kon kon kon   nya o

La colacion
(Christmas Candies)

TEACHER'S PAGE T357

Mexican Folk Song
Piano Accompaniment by Larry Moore

Spanish: Án - da - le a mi - go, - no te di - la - tes, con la ca - nas - ta de los ca - ca - hua - tes. Án - da - le Chon, sal del rin - cón con la ca - nas - ta de la co - la -

English: Come on my friend, and see the pin - a - ta, It's like a bas - ket that holds all our can - dy. Come on, my friend, don't try to hide, We want the sweets that are hid - den in -

ción.
side.

Da - le, da - le da - le,
Aim for the piñ - a - ta,

no pier - das el ti - no,
Try to break it o - pen,

por - que si lo
If you can - not

pier - des,
break it,

pier - des el ca - mi - no.
We will have no can - dy!

An - da - le a -

La ranita cri
(The Little Frog Croaks)

Words and Music by L. Nardelli
English Words by Linda Worsley
Piano Accompaniment by Larry Moore

TEACHER'S PAGE T27

Spanish: La ra - ni - ta Cri el sa - pi - to Cro

English: Lit - tle frog says "cri." Lit - tle toad says "cro."

Sa - len de su ca - sa sa - lu - dan - do al sol.

Com - ing from their house, they greet the morn - ing sun.

Ladybugs' Picnic

TEACHER'S PAGE T290

Music by William Luckey
Words by Don Hadley
Piano Accompaniment by Mark Brymer

Line up 12 "ladybugs" across the front, numbered 1–12. They wave their hand high over head, as if saying "hello," when their number is sung, until all are waving. This should move right down the line.

One two three, four five six,

seven eight nine, ten 'leven twelve,

Put R hand on stomach

la-dy-bugs came,

129

Rub tummy 4 times like "yum yum"

to the la - dy - bugs' pic - nic.

E♭

Wave R hand when number is sung, as before

One two three, four five six, seven eight nine,

E♭

Ladybugs pattycake
Slap legs 2 times   *Clap 2 times*
①   ②   ①   ②

ten 'leven twelve, and they all played games, at the la - dy - bugs'

E♭   B♭

130

Pretend to swing jump rope with both wrists twirling

They played jump rope but the rope it broke so they

Both fists on hips　　　　*Knock R hand 3 times*　　　　*All wave R hand high*

just sat a-round tell-in' knock knock jokes. La - dy - bugs twelve

Rub tummy 4 times

at the la - dy - bugs' pic - nic.

Wave R hand when number is sung, as before

One two three, four five six, seven eight nine,

*With both hands at ear level, open and shut
them 4 times like mouths opening and closing*

Sing 3 times

ten 'leven twelve and they chat-tered a - way at the la - dy - bugs'

B♭

*Rub tummy
4 times*

1., 2.

3.

pic - nic. And they

E♭

B♭ E♭

B♭

E♭

Lavender's Blue

TEACHER'S PAGE T174

Traditional English Song
Piano Accompaniment by Larry Moore

Lav - en - der's blue, dil - ly dil - ly, lav - en - der's green,

when I am King, dil - ly dil - ly, you shall be Queen.

Who told you so, dil - ly dil - ly, who told you so?

'Twas my own heart, dil - ly dil - ly, that told me so.

Let's Go Driving

TEACHER'S PAGE T52

Words and Music by Jeff Moss
Piano Accompaniment by Larry Moore

Pretend to drive a car with both hands, tilt the wheel

1.–5. Let's go driv-ing in an au-to-mo-bile.____ Let's take a ride in a car.____

Cup hand to ear

Drive   *(Repeat actions verses 2–5)*

1. Lis - ten to the mo-tor go vroom vroom vroom___ as we ⎫
2. Lis - ten to the horn___ go beep beep beep___ as we ⎬ trav - el near and far.____
3. Wind - shield___ wi - pers go swish, swish, swish___ as we ⎪
4. Lis - ten to the peo-ple sing La, la, la___ as we ⎪
5. Lis - ten to the sounds___ we all can hear___ as we ⎭

v1: Drive around the room
v2: Drive around the room and honk your horn
v3: Pretend your arms are windshield wipers
v4: Clap side to side on "la"s
v5: Without moving around room, repeat driving, honking horn,
arms as windshield wipers and clapping on "la's according to the lyrics

Library Song

TEACHER'S PAGE T42

Words and Music by Michael Mark and Tom Chapin
Piano Accompaniment by Larry Moore

I'm go-ing down to the li-brar-y, Pick-ing out a book, check it in, check it out.

Gon-na say "Hi," to the dic-tion-ar-y, Pick-ing out a book, check it in, check it out.

Light the Candles

TEACHER'S PAGE T351

Words and Music by Samuel Roeman
Piano Accompaniment by Anna M. Spallina

Joyfully

Hold up R index finger like a candle

Light the lit - tle can - dles, and sing a song for Ha - nuk - kah;

Churn "travel" hands   *Lift Churning hands*   *Present high*

Drei - dels spin - ning gai - ly, for Ha - nuk - kah is here.

Churn "travel" arms

Turn - ing, turn - ing, hor - a dan - cers turn and turn;

Shimmy jazz hands at head level

Burn - ing, burn - ing, see the bright Me - no - rah burn.

Little Black Bug

TEACHER'S PAGE T166

Music by Ruth Boshkoff
Words by Margaret Wise Brown
Piano Accompaniment by Larry Moore

1. "Lit - tle black bug, lit - tle black bug,

Where have you been?" "I've been un - der the

rug." Said the lit - tle black bug.

"Bug, ugh, ugh."

2. "Little green fly, little green fly,
Where have you been?" "I've been way up high."
Said the little green fly. "Buzz, uzz, uzz."

3. "Little old mouse, little old mouse,
Where have you been?" "I've been
all through the house." Said the little
old mouse. "Squeak, eek, eek."

Little Red Caboose

TEACHER'S PAGE T97

Traditional Children's Song
Piano Accompaniment by Carol Jay

Lit - tle red ____ ca - boose, lit - tle red ____ ca - boose,

Lit - tle red ____ ca - boose be - hind the train, ____ the train, ____

Smoke - stack on its back, go - ing down the track.

Lit - tle red ____ ca - boose be - hind the train. Woo - woo - woo!

Little Robin Red Breast

TEACHER'S PAGE T208

English Rhyme
Piano Accompaniment by Larry Moore

142

Looby Loo

TEACHER'S PAGE T262

English Singing Game
Piano Accompaniment by Larry Moore

143

Love Grows

Words and Music by Carol A. Johnson
Piano Accompaniment by Larry Moore

Refrain

Love grows one by one, two by two, and four by four.

Love grows 'round like a cir-cle and comes back knock-in' at your front door.

Verse

Note by note we make a song. Voice by voice we sing it.

D.S. al Fine (Sing Refrain)

Choir by choir we fill up the world with the mu-sic that we bring it.

Love is the Magic Word

TEACHER'S PAGE T366

Words and Music by B.S.
Piano Accompaniment by Larry Moore

Lucy Locket

TEACHER'S PAGE T253

American Song
Piano Accompaniment by Ian Williams

Lu - cy Lock - et lost her pock - et, Kit - ty Fish - er found it.

Not a pen - ny was there in it, On - ly rib - bon 'round it.

Mail Myself to You

TEACHER'S PAGE T366

Words and Music by Woody Guthrie
Piano Accompaniment by William N. Simon

I'm gon-na wrap my-self in pa-per, I'm gon-na daub my-self with glue.

Stick some stamps on top of my head. I'm gon-na mail my-self to you.____

1. I'm a - gon-na tie me up in a red string, I'm gon-na tie blue rib-bons, too;
2. When__ you__ see me in your__ mail-box, Cut the__ string and let me out;
3. Take__ me__ out of my wrap-ping__ pa-per. Wash the__ stamps__ off my head;

I'm a - gon-na climb up in my mail-box, I'm gon-na mail my-self to you.____
Wash__ the__ blue____ off my fin-gers, Stick some__ bub-ble gum in my mouth.__
Pour__ me__ full of ice-cream so-dies, Put me____ in my nice warm bed.__

Martin Luther King

TEACHER'S PAGE T360

Words and Music by Theresa Fulbright
Piano Accompaniment by BIll and Pat Medley

1. He want - ed peace and love all o - ver this
2. He walked for you and me all o - ver this
3. He died for free - dom's cause to save___ this

land, He want - ed peace and love all o - ver this
land, He walked for you and me all o - ver this
land, He died for free - dom's cause to save___ this

land. Mar - tin Lu - ther King was a
land. Mar - tin Lu - ther King was a
land. Mar - tin Lu - ther King was a

peace - lov - ing man, He want - ed peace and love all o - ver this land.
great, geat___ man, He walked for you and me all o - ver this land.
brave, brave___ man, He died for free - dom's cause to save___ this land.

Mary's Coal Black Lamb

TEACHER'S PAGE T286

American Song
Words by Ken Foy
Piano Accompaniment by Larry Moore

1. Mar - y had a lit - tle lamb, lit - tle lamb,
(2.) ev - 'ry - where that Ma - ry went, Mar - y went,

lit - tle lamb. Mar - y had a lit - tle lamb, its
Mar - y went, Ev - 'ry - where that Mar - y went, the

fleece was black as coal. 2. 'Cause big mud hole.
lamb kept fall - ing in a

Mi cuerpo
(My Body)

TEACHER'S PAGE T32

Hispanic Folk Song
English Version by MMH
Piano Accompaniment by Carol Jay

A

C   G 7   C

Spanish: Mi cuer - po, mi cuer - po ha - ce mú - si - ca, Mi
English: My bod - y makes mu - sic, it's eas - y, you will see, My

C   G 7   C   **B**

cuer - po, mi cuer - po ha - ce mú - si - ca. Mis
bod - y makes mu - sic it's eas - y you will see. My

C   F   G 7   C

ma - nos ha - cen (clap clap clap), Mis pi - es ha - can (stamp stamp stamp), Mi
hands, my hands go (clap clap clap), My feet, my feet go (stamp stamp stamp), My

C   F   G 7   C

bo - ca ha - ce "La la la," Mi cuer - po ha - ce "Cha cha cha."
mouth, my mouth goes "La la la," My bod - y does the "Cha cha cha."

150

Miss Mary Mack

African American Singing Game
Piano Accompaniment by WIlliam N. Simon

Mizuguruma
(The Water Wheel)

TEACHER'S PAGE T260

Japanese Game Song
Piano Accompaniment by Larry Moore

Japanese Pronunciation: ka wa no ki wa no mi zu gu ru ma git – chon git – chon
English: **Turn and turn the wat-er wheel by the riv-er-side. "Git-chon, git-chon,"**

ma wa ru min na i so i de fu ta ri zu re
all day long.___ find a part-ner as quick-ly as you can.

no ko re ba o ni yo ichi, ni, san
If you don't find a part-ner, you'll be "It." One, two, three!

My Mama's Calling Me

African American Circle Game
Piano Accompaniment by Larry Moore

My Ma - ma's call - ing me. You can't get out of here. My Ma - ma's call - ing me.

You can't get out of here. What shall I do?___ Pat your ones___ to your knees.

What shall I do?___ Pat your twos___ to your knees. Pat your threes___ to your knees.

Pat your all.

My Mom

TEACHER'S PAGE T372

Words and Music by Cheryl Lavender
Piano Accompaniment by Larry Moore

Na Bahia Tem
(In Bahia Town)

TEACHER'S PAGE T297

Brazilian Folk Song
English Version by Ruth De Cesare
Piano Accompaniment by Larry Moore

Portuguese: **Na Ba - hi - a tem,**
English: **In Ba - hi - a town**

tem, tem, tem, na Ba - hi - a
you will see there's a dark - haired

tem mo - re - na, cô - co de vin - tem.
girl and pen - ny co - co - nut for me.

2. Oh I walked and walked in the sea,
   Looking for a needle but a thimble's all I see.

156

Naranja dulce
(Sweet Orange)

TEACHER'S PAGE T303

Latin American Folk Song
Piano Accompaniment by Larry Moore

Spanish: Na - ran - ja dul - ce, li - món par - ti - do, dá - me un a -
English: Sweet o - range and yel - low le - mon slice, Come and hug me

bra - zo que yo te pi do. Si fue - ra fal - so tu ju - ra -
now, I won't ask you twice, If you make a pro - mise that is - n't

Fine

men - to, en el mo - men - to, te ol - vi - da - ré.
true, In that mo - ment I'll be for - get - ting you.

Na - ran - ja
Sweet o - range

Naughty Kitty Cat

TEACHER'S PAGE T171

Hungarian Folk song
Piano Accompaniment by Larry Moore

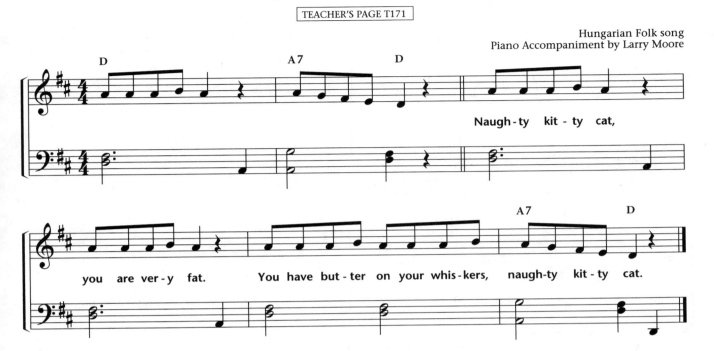

Naugh-ty kit-ty cat, you are ver-y fat. You have but-ter on your whis-kers, naugh-ty kit-ty cat.

159

No One Like You

TEACHER'S PAGE T300

Words and Music by Andra Willis Muhoberac
Piano Accompaniment by Larry Moore

I like your eyes;_____ I like your nose;_____ I like your mouth, your ears, your hands, your toes. I like your face,_____ It's real-ly you; I like the things_____ you say and do. There's not a sin - gle soul who sees the skies the

way you see them through your eyes. And aren't you glad?

You should be glad; There's no one, no one

Ex - act - ly like you.

Old King Glory

TEACHER'S PAGE T217

American Folk Song
Piano Accompaniment by Marilyn Christensen

Old King Glo - ry of the moun - tain, The

moun - tain reached so high, It near - ly reached the sky. The

first one, the sec - ond one, the third fol - low me.

One Little Elephant

TEACHER'S PAGE T194

American Singing Game
Piano Accompaniment by Linda Worsley

1. One Lit - tle El - e - phant went
2. Two Lit - tle El - e - phants went
3. Three Lit - tle El - e - phants went

out to play,
out to play,
out to play,
Out on a spi - der's___ web one day.

He / They had such e - nor - mous fun, He / They called for an - oth - er lit - tle

D   A7   D   G   D   D   G

el - e - phant to come.

D   A7   D

Last time

One, Two, Three, Four, Five

TEACHER'S PAGE T265

American Game Song
Piano Accompaniment by Larry Moore

One, two, three, four, five. Once I caught a fish a - live.

Six, sev - en, eight, nine, ten. Then I let him go a - gain.

Why did you let it go? Be - cause it bit my fin - ger so!
Which fin - ger did it bite? The lit - tle fin - ger on my right!

Over in the Meadow

TEACHER'S PAGE T78

As sung by Margaret Campbelle-Holman
Piano Accompaniment by Carol Jay

1. O - ver in the mea - dow in the sand, in the sun, lived an
2. O - ver in the mea - dow, where the stream runs so blue, lived an
3. O - ver in the mea - dow, in a hole in a tree, lived an

old Moth - er Tur - tle and her lit - tle tur - tle one.
old Moth - er Fish____ and her lit - tle fish - ies two.
old Moth - er Bird____ and her lit - tle bird - ies three.

"Dig," said the moth - er. "I dig," said the one, so he
"Swim," said the moth - er. "We swim," said the two, so they
"Sing," said the moth - er. "We sing," said the three, so they

dug and was glad in the sand, in the sun.
swam and they leaped where the stream runs so blue.
sang and were glad in the hole in the tree.

Pat Pat Patty Pat

Music by Joe Raposo
Words by Jerry Juhl
Piano Accompaniment by Mark Brymer

pat, pat, pat-ty pat, pat-ty, pat-ty, pat, pat - poo!

Cup R hand to R ear while leaning R

Oh, lis - ten to the song that's

Stop

hum-ming in your ear and you'll have more fun than you've had all year. Just

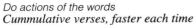

Do actions of the words
Cummulative verses, faster each time

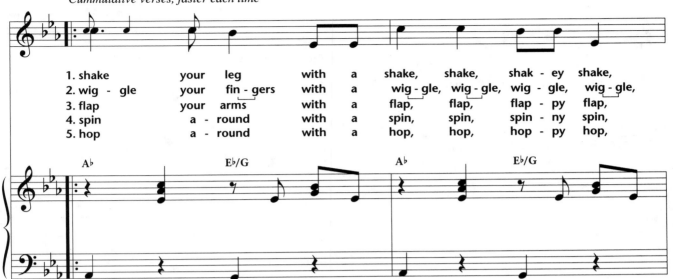

1. shake your leg with a shake, shake, shak - ey shake,
2. wig - gle your fin - gers with a wig - gle, wig - gle, wig - gle, wig - gle,
3. flap your arms with a flap, flap, flap - py flap,
4. spin a - round with a spin, spin, spin - ny spin,
5. hop a - round with a hop, hop, hop - py hop,

First time, no repeat
Use repeat verses 2–5   Pat tummy

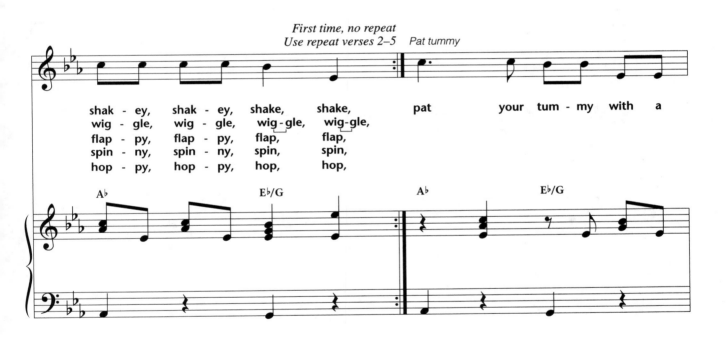

shak - ey, shak - ey, shake, shake, pat your tum - my with a
wig - gle, wig - gle, wig - gle, wig - gle,
flap - py, flap - py, flap, flap,
spin - ny, spin - ny, spin, spin,
hop - py, hop - py, hop, hop,

Last time to Coda

D.S. (4 times) al Coda

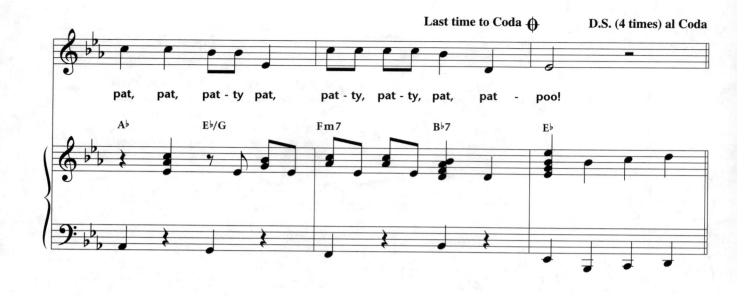

pat,   pat,   pat - ty pat,   pat - ty,   pat - ty,   pat,   pat - poo!

Coda

170

Peanut Butter

TEACHER'S PAGE T218

Camp Song
Piano Accompaniment by Larry Moore

171

Pease Porridge Hot

TEACHER'S PAGRS T255

English Nursery Rhyme
Piano Accompaniment by Carol Jay

1. Pease por - ridge hot,   Pease por - ridge cold,
2. Some like it hot.   Some like it cold.

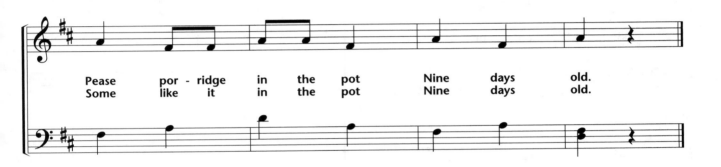

Pease por - ridge in the pot   Nine days old.
Some like it in the pot pot   Nine days old.

Piñón, Pirulín

Mexican Children's Song
Arranged by Gilberto D. Soto
Piano Accompaniment by Larry Moore

Spanish: **Pi** -

ñón, pi - ñón, pi - ñón, pi - ru - lín, pi - ru - lín, pi - ru -

le - ro. Pi - ñón, pi - ñón, pi - ñón, pi - ru -

lín, pi - ru - lín, pi - ru - lón. lón.

2. Miguel, Miguel, Miguel, que la vuelta está a la derecha.
   Miguel, Miguel, Miguel, que la vuelta está al revés.

3. Piñón, piñón, piñón, trole, trole, trolero.
   Miguel, Miguel, Miguel, trole, trole, trole.

Plenty Fishes in the Sea

Children's Song from Dominica
Piano Accompaniment by Larry Moore

Puddle Hopping

TEACHER'S PAGE T60

Music by Steve Horelick
Words by Dennis Kleinman and Janet Weir
Piano Accompaniment by Larry Moore

Woke up this morn - ing, I could see the wind was blow - ing and the rain was drop - ping. _____ No school to - day, Mom's work - ing and my Dad - dy is go - ing shop - ping. _____ What a day! _____ Don't get the blues. _____ Put on your coat _____ and your

rain - y day shoes_____ and go pud - dle hop - ping,_____

pud - dle hop - ping._____ On a day like to - day all my

friends stay in to play, but_____ I'm not stop - ping._____

Look - ing on the ground all a - round till I've found me a pud - dle I can plop in._____

What a way_____ to chase the blues_____ when there's

Pumpkin Song

TEACHER'S PAGE T342

Music by Doug Goodkin
American Rhyme
Piano Accompaniment by Bill and Pat Medley

A pump - kin ran a - way be -

fore Thanks - giv - ing Day. Said he, "They'll make a

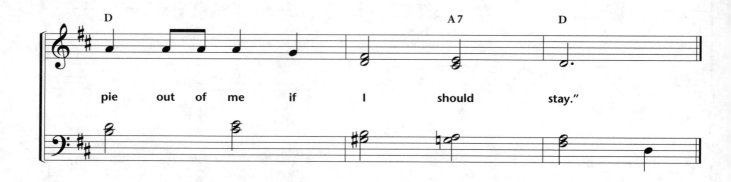

pie out of me if I should stay."

178

Punchinella

TEACHER'S PAGE T216

African-American Game Song
Piano Accompaniment by Larry Moore

nel - la in the shoe? Oh,

We can do it too,___
Look___ can who's___ here,___

Pun - chi - nel - la, Pun - chi - nel - la,

We can do it too,___
Look___ can who's___ here,___

Pun - chi - nel - la in the

shoe.

Pusa't daga
(Cat and Rat)

TEACHER'S PAGE T289

Filipino Folk Song
Collected by Miriam B. Factora
Piano Accompaniment by Larry Moore

Tagalog: Pu - sa ko'y may na - hu - ling da - ga
English: Cat went out and she trapped her a rat!

A - yos ay na - ka - ka - a - wa Meow, meow, meow ang
Rat looked sad, for it was scar - y! "Meow, meow, meow," the

sa - bi ni Ku - ting Di na ki - ta pa - ta - ta - wa - rin.
cat said to the rat. "I'm to catch you, so be war - y."

Put on a Costume

Words and Music by Michael R. Nichols
Piano Accompaniment by Anna Marie Spallina

Put on a cos - tume, wear a mask, we're gon - na trick - or - treat to -

night. Ring the door - bell, hold your bag and give your

neigh - bors all a fright.

Quaker, Quaker

TEACHER'S PAGE T100

American Folk Song
Piano Accompaniment by Larry Moore

"Quak - er, Quak - er, how is thee?" "Ver - y well, I thank thee."

"How's thy neigh - bor next to thee?" "I don't know, I'll go and see."

Rain, Rain, Go Away

TEACHER'S PAGE T259

Traditional Children's Song
Piano Accompaniment by Carol Jay

Rain, rain, go a - way. Come a - gain some oth - er day.

Rain, rain, go a - way. Lit - tle chil - dren want to play.

Rattlesnake

Singing Game
Piano Accompaniment by Larry Moore

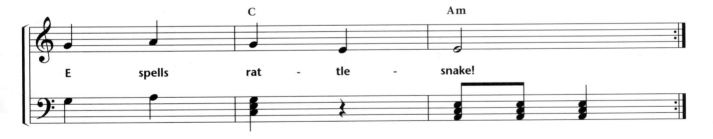

Rig a Jig Jig

TEACHER'S PAGE T116

English Folk Song
Piano Accompaniment by Ian Williams

1.–2. As I was walk-ing down the street, down the street, down the street, { A / A

pret - ty girl } I chanced to meet, Hi - O! Hi - O! Hi - O!
nice young man

Refrain

Rig a jig jig and a - way we go, a - way we go, a - way we go.

Rig a jig jig and a - way we go, Hi - O! Hi - O!____ Hi - O!

Rise, Sally, Rise

TEACHER'S PAGE T162

African American Children's Game
As Sung by Margaret Campbelle-Holman
Piano Accompaniment by Larry Moore

Lit - tle Sal - ly Walk - er sit - tin' in a sau - cer,

Rise, Sal - ly, rise. Ch - ch - ch - ch - ch - ch. Wipe your wee - pin' eyes.

Ch - ch - ch - ch - ch - ch. Shake it to the east and shake it to the west and

shake it to the one that you like the best.

Rudolph, the Red-Nosed Reindeer

TEACHER'S PAGE T354

Words and Music by Johnny Marks
Piano Accompaniment by Bill and Pat Medley

A Sailor Went to Sea, Sea, Sea

TEACHER'S PAGE T38

American Playground Song
Piano Accompaniment by Marilyn Christensen

Sara Watashi
(Plate Passing)

TEACHER'S PAGE T67

Japanese Game Song
Transcribed by Kathy B. sorensen
English Words by Linda Worsley
Piano Accompaniment by Larry Moore

Seeds

TEACHER'S PAGE T120

Words and Music by Laszlo Slomovits
Piano Accompaniment by Larry Moore

See-Saw

TEACHER'S PAGE T242

American Song
Piano Accompaniment by Ian Williams

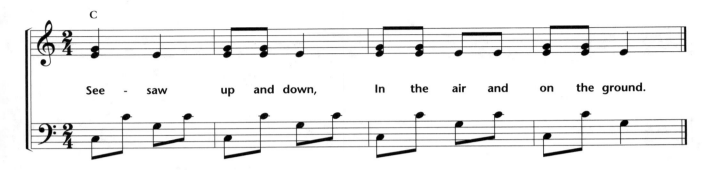

See - saw up and down, In the air and on the ground.

Serra, serra, serrador
(Saw, Saw, Lumberjack)

TEACHER'S PAGE T133

Brazilian Counting Song
English words by Emily Crocker
Piano Accompaniment by Larry Moore

Portuguese: **Ser - ra,**
English: **Saw - ing,**

ser - ra, ser - ra - dor. Quan - tos paus o se - nhor ser - ron? Un,
saw - ing, lum - ber - jack. How many logs____ will you stack? One,

dos, tres, qua - tro, cin - co, seis, se - te, oi - to, no - ve, dez!
two, three, four,____ five,____ six, sev - en, eight,____ nine,____ ten!

Sesame Street

TEACHER'S PAGE T298

Music by Joe Raposo
Words by Bruce Hart, Jon Stone, and Joe Raposo
Piano Accompaniment by Mark Brymer

Shoo, Turkey

TEACHER'S PAGE T76

Written and Adapted by Bessie Jones
Piano Accompaniment by Larry Moore

Lit-tle girl, lit-tle boy? Yes, Ma'am. Well, did you go down town?___ Yes, Ma'am. Well, did you get an-y eggs? Yes, Ma'am. Well, did you bring them home? Yes, Ma'am. Well, did you cook an-y bread? Yes, Ma'am. Well, did you

Sing After Me

TEACHER'S PAGE T34

Music by Sam Pottle
Words by Tony Geiss
Piano Accompaniment by Mark Brymer

Sittin' Down to Eat

TEACHER'S PAGE T182

Words and Music by Bill Harley
Piano Accompaniment by Larry Moore

you gon-na do? You got e-nough for one, you got e-nough for two. I've

got e-nough for me, yes_____ that's true._____ If I've got e-nough for me, I guess I've

got e - nough for you."_____

Six Little Ducks

TEACHER'S PAGE T64

American Game Song
Piano Accompaniment by Larry Moore

1. Six lit - tle ducks that I once knew, Fat ones, skin - ny ones,
2. Down to the riv - er they would go, Wibble, wobble, wib - ble, wobble,

fair ones too,} But the one lit - tle duck with a feath - er in {1. her 2. his} back,
to and fro,}

{1. She 2. He} led the oth - ers with a quack, quack, quack.

Skin and Bones

TEACHER'S PAGE T340

Kentucky Folk Song
Collected by Jean Ritchie
Piano Accompaniment by MMH

1. There was an old wom-an all skin and bones,
2. She lived____ down by____ the old grave - yard,
3. One night____ she thought__ she'd old take a walk.

Oo - oo - oo - ooh!

4. She walked down by the old
   graveyard, Oo-oo-oo-oh!

5. She was the bones a-layin'
   around, Oo-oo-oo-oh!

6. She went to the closet to get a
   broom, Oo-oo-oo-oh!

7. She opened the door and BOO!

Skip to My Lou

TEACHER'S PAGE T102

American Play Song
Piano Accompaniment by Marilyn Christensen

1. Flies in the but-ter-milk, Shoo fly, shoo, Flies in the but-ter-milk,
2. Lit-tle red wag - on paint - ed blue, Lit-tle red wag - on

Shoo fly, shoo, Flies in the but - ter - milk, Shoo fly, shoo,
paint - ed blue, Lit-tle red wag - on paint - ed blue,

Skip to my lou, my dar - ling.

3. Lost my partner, what'll I do?

4. I'll find another one, better than you;...

5. Lou, lou, skip to my lou;...

213

Sleep Bonnie Bairnie

TEACHER'S PAGE T26

Newcastle Lullaby
Piano Accompaniment by Larry Moore

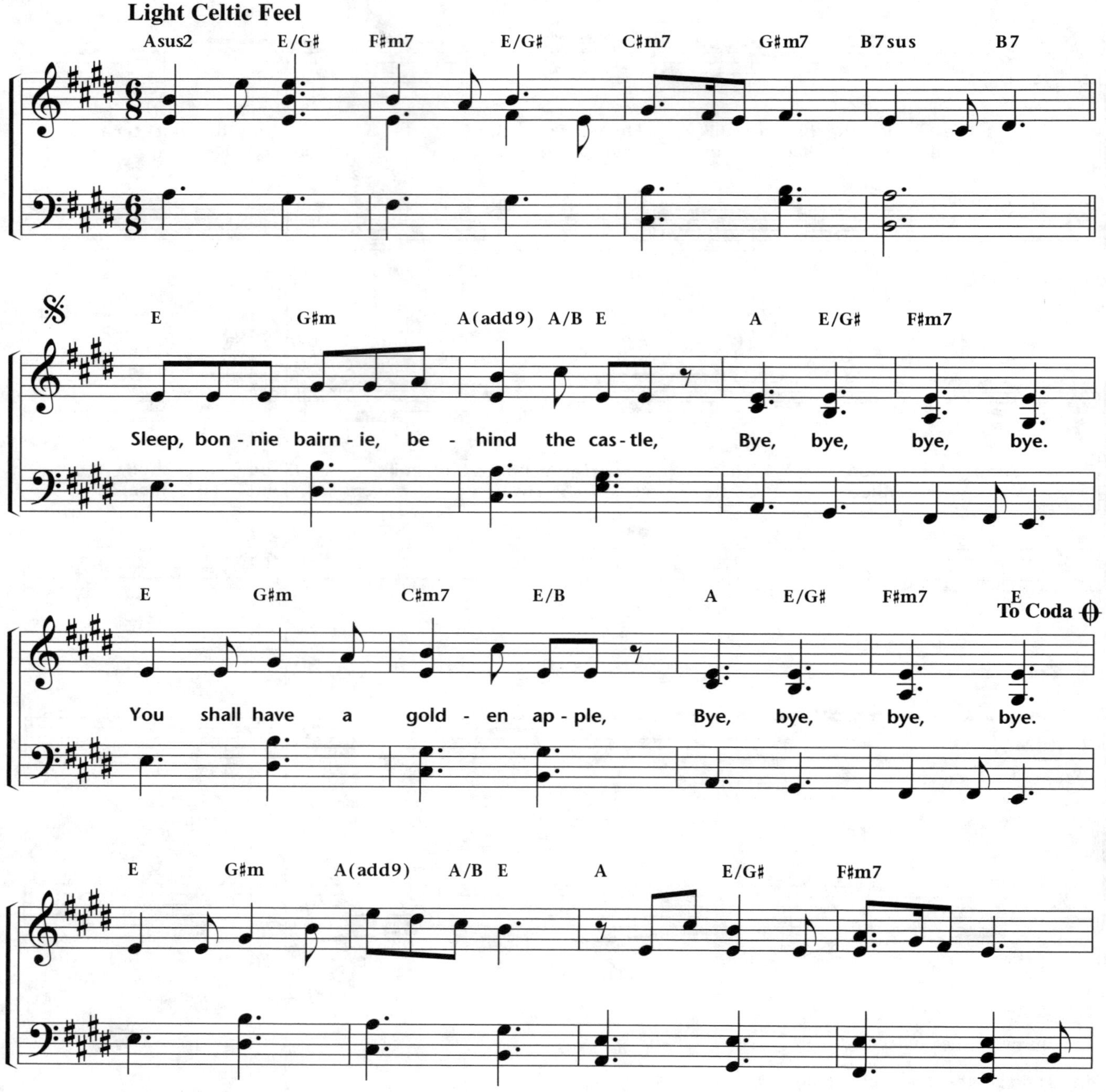

Light Celtic Feel
Asus2 E/G♯ F♯m7 E/G♯ C♯m7 G♯m7 B7sus B7
E G♯m A(add9) A/B E A E/G♯ F♯m7
Sleep, bon - nie bairn - ie, be - hind the cas - tle, Bye, bye, bye, bye.
E G♯m C♯m7 E/B A E/G♯ F♯m7 E
To Coda
You shall have a gold - en ap - ple, Bye, bye, bye, bye.
E G♯m A(add9) A/B E A E/G♯ F♯m7

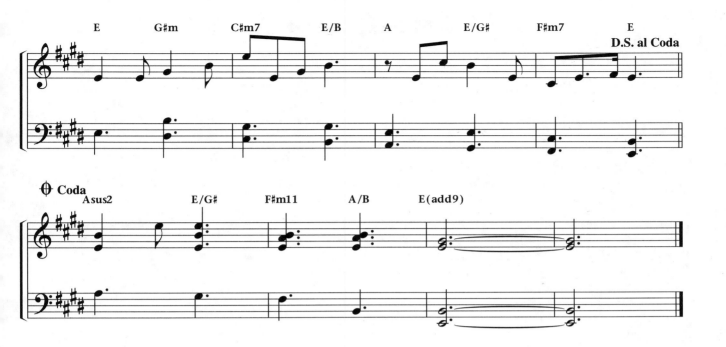

Snail, Snail

TEACHER'S PAGE T252

American Singing Game
Piano Accompaniment by Marilyn Christensen

Snail, snail, snail, snail, 'Round and 'round and 'round and 'round.

Snail with the Mail

TEACHER'S PAGE T275

Words by Robert Reale
Music by Willie Reale
Piano Accompaniment by Stacey Nordmeyer

Slap hips

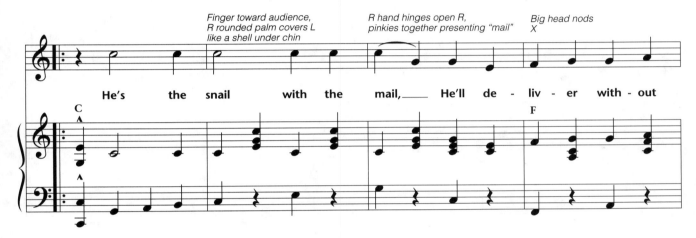

*Finger toward audience,
R rounded palm covers L
like a shell under chin*

*R hand hinges open R,
pinkies together presenting "mail"*

Big head nods

He's the snail with the mail, He'll de-liv-er with-out

*Hands straight up,
fingers "rain" down for 8 counts*

fail in the rain or sleet or snow. No

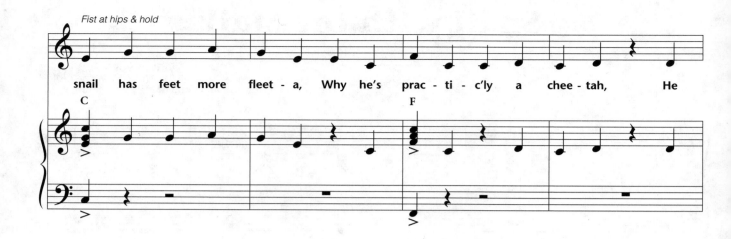

Fist at hips & hold

snail has feet more fleet - a, Why he's prac - ti - c'ly a chee - tah, He

Fist grab "steering wheel"

puts the "go" in es - car - got. got.

1. Twist "wheel"
R L R
X X X

2. Repeat "wheel" twist
R L R
X X X
Repeat "shell" position
X

Somebody Come and Play

TEACHER'S PAGE T92

Words and Music by Joe Raposo
Piano Accompaniment by Mark Brymer

1. Some-bod-y come and play.
2. Some-bod-y come and play.

Some-bod-y come and play to - day._____ Some-bod-y come and
Some-bod-y come and play my way._____ Some-bod-y come and

219

220

Something Funny Outside

Music by Betty Barlow
Words by Betty Barlow and Victoria Shima
Piano Accompaniment by Ian WIlliams

breath - ing.   Lis - ten!   I can hear   some - thing fun - ny out -

side!   It's   here!

*For two beats, a few children create scary noises - vocal or otherwise.

Soup, Soup

TEACHER'S PAGE T358

African American Singing Game
Piano Accompaniment by Larry Moore

Spring

Words by Robert Reale
Music by Willie Reale

Star Light, Star Bright

Traditional
Piano Accompaniment by Larry Moore

Star - light,   star   bright,   First   star   I   see   to - night,   I

wish   I   may,   I   wish   I   might,   Have   the   wish   I   wish   to - night.

1

S'vivon Sov
(Dreidel Spin)

Jewish Folk Song
Piano Accompaniment by Larry Moore

Tak for maden
(Thanks for Food)

TEACHER'S PAGE T343

Danish Folk Song
Piano Accompaniment by Bill and Pat Medley

Danish/Engligh: Tak for ma - den, tak for ma - den, Bless this food we pray.

Tak for ma - den, ta for ma - den, Thank Thee, Lord, to - day.

Strength-en, love, and guide us. Stay Thou close be - side us:

Tak for ma - den, tak for ma - den, Bless ths food we pray.

Tako No Uta
(The Kite Song)

TEACHER'S PAGE T370

Japanese Folk Song
English Version by MMH
Piano Accompaniment by Bill and Pat Medley

Japanese Pronunciation: ta ko ta ko a ga ɾe
English: **Sail** up,____ **kite,** **in** - **to** **the** **sky!**

ka ze yo ku u ke te
While **the** **wind** **is** **blow** - **ing** **high,**

ku mo ma de a ga ɾe
Soar **up**____ **high** **a** - **bove** **the** **clouds;**

te n ma de a ga ɾe
To **the** **hea** - **vens,** **fly** **so** **high!**

232

There Are Many Flags In Many Lands

TEACHER'S PAGE T329

Composer Unknown
Words by M.H. Howliston
Piano Accompaniment by Larry Moore

Verse

There are man-y flags in man-y lands, there are flags of ev-'ry hue; But there is no flag, how-ev-er grand, Like our own Red, White and Blue.

Refrain

Then hur-rah for the flag, Our coun-try's flag, It's stripes and white stars, too; For there is no flag in an-y land, Like our own Red, White and Blue.

There's a Hole in the Middle of the Sea

TEACHER'S PAGE T178

Singing Game
Piano Accompaniment by Larry Moore

cumulative verses

2. There's a log in the hole
   in the middle of the sea.
   There's a log in the hole
   in the middle of the sea.
   There's a log, there's a log,
   there's a log in the hole
   in the middle of the sea.

3. There's a bump on the log
   in the hole in the middle
   of the sea...

4. There's a frog on the bump
   on the log in the hole
   in the middle of the sea...

5. There's a fly on the frog
   on the bump on the log
   in the hole in the middle
   of the sea...

6. There's a wing on the fly
   on the frog on the bump
   on the log in the hole
   in the middle of the sea...

7. There's a flea on the wing
   on the fly on the frog
   on the bump on the log
   in the hole in the middle
   of the sea...

234

This Little Light of Mine

TEACHER'S PAGE T238

African American spiritual
Piano Accompaniment by Tom Anderson

This Old Man

English Game Song
Piano Accompaniment by Kryste Andrews

1. This old man, he played one,
2. This old man, he played two,

He played nick - nack on my drum, } With a
He played nick - nack on my shoe,

nick - nack pad - dy whack, give a dog a bone,

This old man came roll - ing home.

3. ...three,...tree...

4. ...four,...door...

5. ...five,...hive,...

6. ...six,...sticks...

7. ...seven,...oven...

8. ...eight,...gate,...

9. ...nine,...line...

10. ...ten,...hen...

A Time for Love

TEACHER'S PAGE T347

Adapted from Nancy Dervan
Piano Accompaniment by Ian Williams

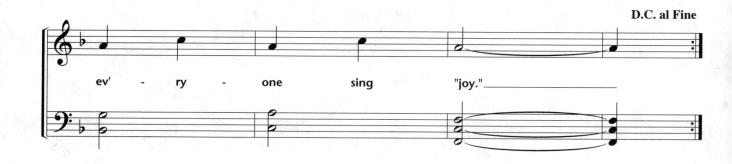

ev' - ry - one sing "joy." _____

Tinker, Tailor

TEACHER'S PAGE T130

Piano Accompaniment by Larry Moore

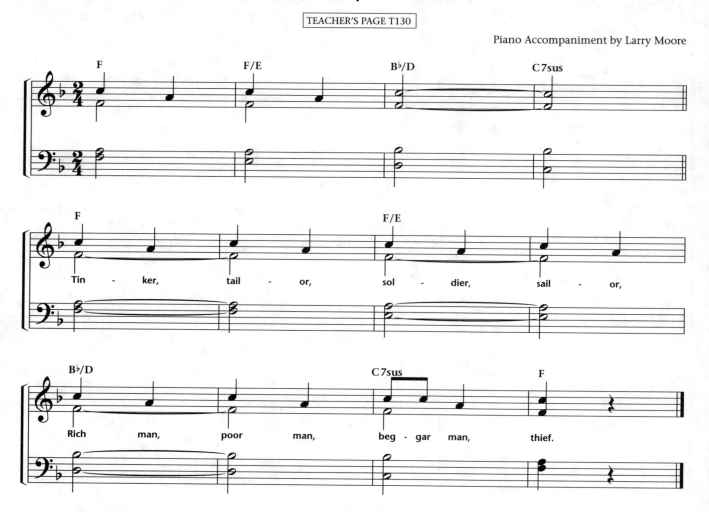

Tin - ker, tail - or, sol - dier, sail - or,

Rich man, poor man, beg - gar man, thief.

238

Twenty-four Robbers

TEACHER'S PAGE T173

Piano Accompaniment by Larry Moore

Not last night, but the night be - fore, twen-ty-four rob - bers at my door.

I got up to let them in. Put 'em all in the gar - bage bin!

Two, Four, Six, Eight

TEACHER'S PAGE T246

Engligh Nursery Rhyme
Music by Marilyn Copland Davidson
Piano Accompaniment by Anna M. Spallina

Two, four, six, eight, Meet me at the gar - den gate.

*If I'm late, don't wait. Two, four, six, eight.

*You may wish to speak this phrase.

240

Uga Uga Uga
(Cake, Cake, Cake)

TEACHER'S PAGE T313

Israeli Melody
Words by Aharon Ashman
Piano Accompaniment by Larry Moore

Una adivinanza
(A Riddle)

TEACHER'S PAGE T138

Traditional Mexican Riddle
Piano Accompaniment by Larry Moore

Spanish: U - na se - ño - ra muy a - se - ño - ra - da
English: One love - ly la - dy a ver - y pro - per la - dy,

lle - va go - rro ver - de_y ca - mi - sa co - lo - ra da
On her head a green cap and on her back a red shirt.

¡A - di - vi - na lo que es! Fre - sa, fre - sa.
Can you tell me what she is? Straw - berry! Straw - berry!

Viva Valentine!

TEACHER'S PAGE T364

Words and Music by Teresa Jennings
Piano Accompaniment by Larry Moore

L - E - N   L - E - N   T - I - N - E   T - I - N - E   Vi - va Val - en - tine!   Oh!

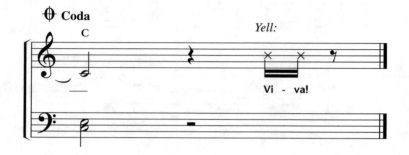

Coda

Yell:

Vi - va!

Wake Me, Shake Me

TEACHER'S PAGE T199

American Folk song
Piano Accompaniment by Larry Moore

Wake me! Shake me!

Don't let me sleep too late! Got-ta get up bright and ear-ly in the morn-ing. Gon-na

swing on the Gold-en Gate.

We All Sing with the Same Voice

Music by J. Philip Miller
Words by Sheppard M. Green and J. Philip Miller
Piano Accompaniment by Larry Moore

246

Refrain

247

What's Your Name?

TEACHER'S PAGE T125

American Game Song
Piano Accompaniment by Larry Moore

What's your name? Pud - ding Tame.

Ask me a - gain and I'll tell you the same.

same.

When the Flag Goes By

TEACHER'S PAGE T327

Words and Music by Lynn Freeman Olson
Piano Accompaniment by Larry Moore

Willum

American Folk Song
Piano Accompaniment by Larry Moore

1. Wil - lum he had sev - en sons, sev - en sons, sev - en sons.
2. Num - ber one was chip - ping wood, chip - ping wood, chip - ping wood.
3. Num - ber two jumped up and down, up and down, up and down.
4. Num - ber three a - danc - ing went, danc - ing went, danc - ing went.

Wil - lum he had sev - en sons and this is what they did.
Num - ber one was chop - ping wood and this is what he did.
Num - ber two jumped up and down, and this is what he did.
Num - ber three a - danc - ing went and this is what he did.

5. Number four was hammering, hammering, hammering.
   Number four was hammering and this is what he did.

6. Number five was painting, painting, painting.
   Number five was painting and this is what he did.

7. Number six was clapping, clapping, clapping.
   Number six was clapping and this is what he did.

8. Number seven was napping, napping, napping.
   Number seven was napping and this is what he did.

Repeat Verse 1

The Wind Blew East

TEACHER'S PAGE T234

Folk Song fron the Bahamas
Piano Accompaniment by Carol Jay

252

Wind Blow

TEACHER'S PAGE T187

Words and Music by Eva Abejón
Piano Accompaniment by Larry Moore

Wind blow, wind blow, blow all o - ver move the air. Wind blow, wind blow, blow a-round me and my friends.

A Year with Frog and Toad

TEACHER'S PAGE T270

Words by Robert Reale
Music by Willie Reale
Piano Accompaniment by Stacey Nordmeyer

255

256

A Year with Frog and Toad Reprise

TEACHER'S PAGE T283

Words by Robert Reale
Music by Willie Reale

258

Yo, Mamana, Yo
(Oh, Mama, Oh)

TEACHER'S PAGE T307

Shangaan Folk Song
Piano Accompaniment by Larry Moore

Shangaan: Yo ma - ma - na yo,
English: Oh, ma - ma_____ oh,

Yo ma - ma - na yo,
Oh ma - ma_____ oh.

Un - ga fam - ba u - ni
Oh, if on - ly you were

si - ya.
here now,

U - ni si - ye - la
I could fall a - sleep

vusi - wa - na.
once a - gain.

Zui, Zui, Zukkorbashi
(Mouse in the Rice Sack)

Japanese Game Song
Transcribed by Kathy B. Sorensen
English Words by Linda Worsley
Piano Accompaniment by Larry Moore

TEACHER'S PAGE T98

Acknowledgments

Creative Direction and Delivery: The Quarasan Group, Inc.
The Broadway Junior® logo and MTI® logo are trademarks of Music Theatre International. All Rights Reserved. Grateful acknowledgment is given to the following authors, composers, and publishers. Every effort has been made to trace the ownership of all copyrighted material and to secure the necessary permissions to reprint these selections. In the case of some selections for which acknowledgment is not given, extensive research has failed to locate the copyright holders.

Songs and Speech Pieces

Autumn Leaves Are Falling, Words and Music by Mary Donnelly and George L.O. Strid. Copyright © 1999 by HAL LEONARD CORPORATION. International Copyright Secured. All Rights Reserved.

Best Friends, Words and Music by Sandor Slomovits. Copyright © Sandor Slomovits. International Copyright Secured. All Rights Reserved.

Big and Small, by Ellen McCullough Brabson. Used by Permission.

Boris the Singing Bear, Words and Music by Jackie Silberg. Copyright © 1996 by Miss Jackie Music Company. International Copyright Secured. All Rights Reserved.

Brush Your Teeth, Words and Music by Raffi Cavoukian, Kenneth David Whitely and Dain Louise, Copyright © by Homeland Publishing, a div. of Troubadour Music, Inc. International Copyright Secured. All Rights Reserved.

Butterfly, Flutter By, Words and Music by Linda Worsley. Copyright © Ganymede Music Productions. International Copyright Secured. All Rights Reserved.

Caribbean Amphibian, Words and Music by Mark Saltzman. Copyright © 1986 Sesame Street Music, Inc. All Rights Administered by Sony/ATV Music Publishing, 8 Music Square West, Nashville, TN 37203. International Copyright Secured. All Rights Reserved.

Chickery Chick, Words by Sylvia Dee. Music by Sidney Lippman. Copyright © 1945 by Santly Joy, Inc. Copyright Renewed and Assigned to Universal—PolyGram International Publishing, Inc. International Copyright Secured. All Rights Reserved.

Cookies, From MTI's Broadway Junior Broadway for Kids A YEAR WITH FROG AND TOAD JUNIOR. Music by Robert Reale. Lyrics by Willie Reale. Copyright © Fratelli Reale Music (ASCAP).

Counting Song, Copyright © by Alfred Publishing Co., Inc. International Copyright Secured. All Rights Reserved. Used by Permission.

Cut the Cake, The Singing Book Second Level by Mary Alice Hein and Lois Choksy. Copyright © 1983 by Mary Alice Hein, S.N.J.M. and Lois Choksy. Pub. by Renna/White Associates. All Rights Reserved.

Dance Myself to Sleep, Words and Music by Norman Stiles and Christopher Cerf. Copyright © 1981 Sesame Street Music, Inc. and Splotched Animal Music. All Rights on behalf of Sesame Street Music, Inc. Administered by Sony/ATV Music Publishing, 8 Music Square West, Nashville, TN 37203. International Copyright Secured. All Rights Reserved.

Down the Hill, From MTI's Broadway Junior Broadway for Kids A YEAR WITH FROG AND TOAD JUNIOR. Music by Robert Reale. Lyrics by Willie Reale. Copyright © Fratelli Reale Music (ASCAP).

Duérmete mi niño (Go to Sleep, My Baby), Puerto Rican Folk Song. Adapted by José-Lúis Orozco, Copyright © 1996 by José-Lúis Orozco/Arcoiris Records, P.O. Box 461900, Los Angeles, CA 90046. International Copyright Secured. English Words by Macmillan/McGraw-Hill. All Rights Reserved.

George Washington, Words and Music by Lynn Freeman Olson. Copyright © 1964 (Renewed 1992) by Alfred Publishing Co., Inc. International Copyright Secured. All Rights Reserved. Used by Permission.

Goin' to the Zoo, Words and Music by Tom Paxton. Copyright © 1961. Renewed 1989. Cherry Lane Music Publishing Company, Inc. (ASCAP) and DreamWorks Songs (ASCAP). Worldwide Rights for DreamWorks Songs Administered by Cherry Lane Music Publishing Company, Inc. International Copyright Secured. All Rights Reserved.

Halloween (You Should Know . . .), Words and Music by Lynn Freeman Olson. Copyright © 1966, 1971 (Renewed 1994, 1998) by Holt, Rinehart & Winston. International Copyright Secured. All Rights Reserved.

Happiest Street in the World, The, Words and Music by Joe Raposo. Copyright © 1979 by Wizzybus Music, Inc. International Copyright Secured. All Rights Reserved.

Teacher's Notes

Teacher's Notes

Teacher's Notes

Teacher's Notes

Teacher's Notes

Teacher's Notes

Alphabetical Song Index